A2 Biology

You've made it through AS Biology, so now's the time to start thinking about A2.
And with modules to take as early as January, you need to
make sure you hit the ground running.

This book will give you a Head Start — it covers topics you'll study
at A2 that you haven't covered since GCSE, and includes loads of
practice questions to make sure you've got the hang of it all.

Spend the first week back in 6th form or (whisper it quietly) the summer holiday working
through it so everything will make perfect sense when you start your A2.

We've done our bit — the rest is up to you.

06435

What CGP is all about

Our sole aim here at CGP is to produce the highest quality books
— carefully written, immaculately presented and dangerously
close to being funny.

Then we work our socks off to get them out to you
— at the cheapest possible prices.

Contents

Section One — Photosynthesis and Respiration

Section Two — Energy Flow in Ecosystems

Section Three — Nutrient Cycles and Global Warming

Section Four — Inheritance

Section Five — Communication

Section Six — Homeostasis

Section Seven — Protein Synthesis

Section Eight — Gene Technology

Section Nine — Investigating and Interpreting

Published by Coordination Group Publications Ltd.

Contributors:
Ellen Bowness, Charlotte Burrows,
Barbara Green, Jane Towle

With thanks to Joe Brazier and Sue Hocking
for the proofreading.

Graph to show trend in atmospheric CO_2 concentration
and global temperature on page 15 based on data by EPICA
Community Members 2004 and Siegenthaler et al 2005.

ISBN: 978 1 84762 344 7
Groovy website: www.cgpbooks.co.uk
Jolly bits of clipart from CorelDRAW®
Printed by Elanders Hindson Ltd, Newcastle upon Tyne.
Text, design, layout and original illustrations
© Coordination Group Publications Ltd. 2009
All rights reserved.

Photosynthesis

Chloroplasts are the Site of Photosynthesis

1) _Photosynthesis_ is the process by which _light energy_ is converted into _chemical energy_ (in the form of _glucose_). It _happens in chloroplasts_.

2) Chloroplasts _contain chlorophyll_, which is a green pigment that _absorbs light energy._

3) _Not all_ plant cells contain chloroplasts (e.g. most roots are not green) — it would be a waste of energy and materials for plants to produce chloroplasts for cells that don't receive light.

4) Photosynthesis is a _series of reactions_, but the _overall_ equation is:

> Word equation: CARBON DIOXIDE + WATER + ENERGY → GLUCOSE + OXYGEN
>
> Symbol equation: $6CO_2$ + $6H_2O$ + ENERGY → $C_6H_{12}O_6$ + $6O_2$

Chloroplasts are Full of Membranes

1) A chloroplast has a _double membrane_ — an _outer_ membrane and an _inner_ membrane.

2) It also contains membrane-bound sacs called _thylakoids_ (pronounced: thile-ack-oids). Many chlorophyll molecules are embedded in the thylakoid membranes.

3) A stack of thylakoids is called a _granum_ (grah-num). The plural of granum is _grana_.

4) The thylakoids of one granum may be _connected_ to other grana.

5) The _fluid_ in which the grana are suspended is called the _stroma_.

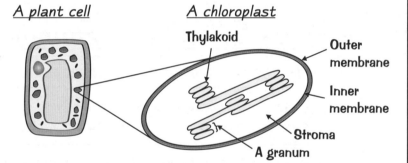

A plant cell   A chloroplast

Thylakoid

Outer membrane

Inner membrane

Stroma

A granum

Photosynthesis Takes Place in Two Stages

1) In the _first stage_ of photosynthesis, chlorophyll molecules absorb light energy, which is transferred to protein molecules in the thylakoid membranes to produce ATP (the energy is _stored in ATP_).

2) The _second stage_ takes place in the _stroma_. The ATP is used to convert _carbon dioxide_ to _glucose_.

Four questions to get you started:

1) Name the chemical in chloroplasts that absorbs light energy.
2) How many membranes are around a chloroplast?
3) What is a stack of thylakoids called?
4) In which part of a chloroplast is carbon dioxide converted to glucose?

Answers
1) Chlorophyll.
2) Two (an outer membrane and an inner membrane).
3) A granum.
4) In the stroma.

Respiration

Glucose is Used in Respiration

1) Respiration is the process of _releasing energy from glucose_.
2) Energy is needed by organisms for loads of things, for example:
   - Muscle contraction
   - Making proteins
   - Maintaining body temperature.
3) _Plants get glucose_ for respiration _from photosynthesis_.
4) _Animals_ have to _eat_ plants or other animals to _get glucose_ for respiration.

The chemical energy trapped in glucose is released by respiration for use by the organism.

All Organisms Carry Out Respiration

Don't forget that _plants AND animals AND microorganisms_ (except viruses) all carry out _respiration_.
But _only plants photosynthesise_.

Some algae and a few bacteria also carry out photosynthesis, but you don't need to worry about them.

There are Two Types of Respiration

1) The two types of respiration are _aerobic_ and _anaerobic_:

   - _Aerobic_ respiration is respiration _using oxygen_.
   - _Anaerobic_ respiration is respiration _without using oxygen_.

2) Some organisms _just_ carry out _aerobic_ respiration, some _just_ carry out _anaerobic_ respiration and some can _do both_, e.g. humans.
3) _Anaerobic_ respiration _doesn't release as much energy_ from a molecule of glucose as aerobic respiration does.

Aerobic Respiration Starts with Glycolysis

Aerobic respiration is a _series of reactions_, but the overall equation is:

Word equation: GLUCOSE + OXYGEN → CARBON DIOXIDE + WATER + ENERGY

Symbol equation: $C_6H_{12}O_6$ + $6O_2$ → $6CO_2$ + $6H_2O$ + ENERGY

1) The _first stage_ of aerobic respiration is called _glycolysis_ (gly-kol-i-sis). It takes place in the _cytoplasm_ of cells.
2) In glycolysis each 6-carbon _glucose_ molecule ($C_6H_{12}O_6$) is _split_ into two _3-carbon pyruvate_ (pie-roo-vate) molecules by a series of reactions.
3) A _small amount_ of _energy_ is _released_ during glycolysis.

Respiration

The Next Stages Take Place in Mitochondria

1) The _pyruvate_ molecules produced from glycolysis then pass _into_ the centre (the _matrix_) of the _mitochondria_. This is where the next stages (more chemical reactions) take place.
2) During these reactions _carbon dioxide_ and _water_ are released as _waste products_.
3) A _large amount_ of _energy_ is _released_ during these reactions.

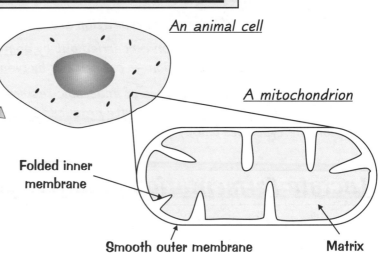

An animal cell

A mitochondrion

Folded inner membrane

Smooth outer membrane

Matrix

The Energy Released is used to Make ATP

1) The _energy_ released from glycolysis and the other stages of respiration is used to _make molecules of ATP_. _Most_ of the ATP is made at the folded, _inner membrane_ of the mitochondria.
2) The _energy is used_ to add a _phosphate group_ (P_i) to a molecule of _adenosine diphosphate_ (ADP) to make a molecule of _adenosine triphosphate_ (ATP).
3) The ATP then _moves_ to where energy is needed in the cell.
4) It's then _broken down_ back into ADP and P_i, which _releases energy_.
5) So ATP acts like a kind of energy delivery boy in the cell.

$$\text{ADP} + P_i \underset{\text{Energy released}}{\overset{\text{Energy used}}{\rightleftharpoons}} \text{ATP}$$

Understanding respiration isn't easy — have a go at these questions:

1) Define respiration.
2) State two processes that energy released from respiration is used for.
3) Which type of respiration releases less energy per molecule of glucose?
4) Give the symbol equation for aerobic respiration.
5) What is the name of the first stage in aerobic respiration?
6) What two reactants combine to make ATP?

Respiration

There are Two Types of Anaerobic Respiration

1) The two types of anaerobic respiration are:
   - <u>Lactate</u> fermentation — carried out by <u>animals</u> and <u>some bacteria</u>.
   - <u>Alcoholic</u> fermentation — carried out by <u>plants</u> and <u>yeast</u>.

2) The <u>first stage</u> in both types of anaerobic respiration is <u>glycolysis</u>, but what happens to the <u>pyruvate</u> produced by glycolysis depends on the type (see below).

Lactate Fermentation Produces Lactic Acid

1) In lactate fermentation, the <u>pyruvate</u> that's produced by glycolysis is converted into <u>lactic acid</u>.

> GLUCOSE ➜ PYRUVATE + a small amount of energy
> PYRUVATE ➜ LACTIC ACID

2) This process allows glycolysis to <u>keep going</u> when there's <u>no oxygen</u>, releasing a <u>small amount</u> of <u>energy</u>.

3) In humans, lactic acid quickly <u>dissociates</u> (breaks down) into <u>hydrogen</u> ions (H^+) and <u>lactate</u> ions. Lactate is then converted <u>back to pyruvate</u> when <u>oxygen</u> is available.

> LACTIC ACID ➜ H^+ + LACTATE$^-$

Lactate fermentation occurs in <u>animal muscle cells</u> during strenuous <u>exercise</u>.

Alcoholic Fermentation Produces Ethanol

1) In alcoholic fermentation, the <u>pyruvate</u> that's produced by glycolysis is converted into <u>ethanol</u> (a type of alcohol).

> GLUCOSE ➜ PYRUVATE + a small amount of energy
> PYRUVATE ➜ ETHANOL + CO_2

2) This process also allows glycolysis to <u>keep going</u> when there's <u>no oxygen</u>, releasing a <u>small amount</u> of <u>energy</u>.

Another mini quiz to get your teeth into:

1) Which organisms carry out lactate fermentation?
2) What is the first stage of alcoholic fermentation?
3) What is pyruvate converted to during lactate fermentation?
4) What does anaerobic respiration in yeast produce?

Answers
1) Animals and some bacteria.
2) Glycolysis.
3) Lactic acid (lactate).
4) Ethanol and CO_2 (yeast carry out alcoholic fermentation).

Energy Flow and Food Chains

Energy Moves Between the Organisms in an Ecosystem

1) An <u>ecosystem</u> is <u>all</u> the <u>organisms</u> in a place and all the other <u>non-living factors</u> that are there, e.g. a forest ecosystem includes all the trees, plants, animals and microorganisms in the forest and all the water, soil, rock and air in it too.

2) Energy <u>enters</u> an ecosystem by <u>photosynthesis</u> — plants convert <u>sunlight energy</u> into a form that can be <u>used</u> by other organisms.

3) <u>Energy flows</u> (moves) between all the organisms in an ecosystem.

4) Organisms <u>use energy to grow</u>, so energy is <u>stored</u> in their <u>bodies</u>.

5) This energy is <u>passed on</u> when the organism is <u>eaten</u>. E.g. a plant uses energy from the sun to <u>grow new leaves</u>. The energy stored in the leaves <u>moves</u> into a rabbit when the <u>rabbit eats the plant</u>. The rabbit uses some of that energy to <u>grow new muscle tissue</u>. The energy stored in the rabbit muscle tissue moves into a fox when the <u>fox eats the rabbit</u>.

Each Stage in a Food Chain is a Trophic (Feeding) Level

1) How the energy moves between the organisms in an ecosystem can be shown using <u>food chains</u> and <u>food webs</u>.

2) Food chains and food webs basically show <u>which organisms eat which others</u> in an ecosystem, so each <u>stage</u> in a food chain or web is called a <u>trophic (feeding) level</u>.

3) <u>Producers</u> occupy (make up) the <u>first level</u> in a food chain or web.

4) <u>Primary consumers</u> (herbivores) occupy the next level — they <u>eat producers</u>.

5) <u>Secondary</u> consumers (carnivores and omnivores) occupy the next level — they <u>eat primary consumers</u>.

6) <u>Tertiary</u> consumers occupy the next level — they <u>eat secondary consumers</u> (and so on).

7) <u>Food chains</u> are quite simple — they show <u>one way</u> the energy from a producer is passed to the last consumer.

Dandelion	Rabbit	Fox
Producer	Primary consumer	Secondary consumer

Is eaten by → Is eaten by →

> The amount of energy available at each level <u>decreases</u> as you go <u>along</u> a food chain (see next page) — so you <u>don't</u> usually get <u>more than 5</u> trophic levels.

8) <u>Food webs</u> are more complicated — they show <u>multiple food chains</u> so they show <u>loads of different ways</u> energy flows (moves) through an ecosystem:

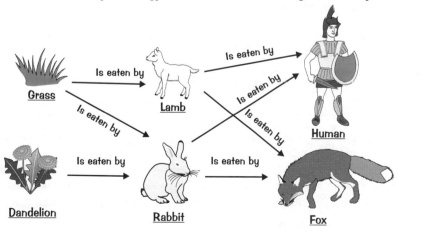

Energy Flow and Food Chains

Some Energy is Lost at Each level in a Food Chain

As you go _up_ the _trophic levels_ in a food chain, the _amount of energy_ at each level _decreases_. Energy is _lost at_ each level and _between_ each level in various ways:

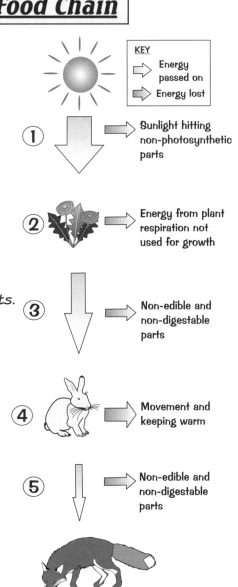

KEY
⇨ Energy passed on
⇨ Energy lost

1) Energy is lost _between_ sunlight and the producer:
   - Some Sunlight will fall on areas of the plant that _don't photosynthesise_, e.g. the stem or trunk.

   ① Sunlight hitting non-photosynthetic parts

2) Energy is lost _from_ the _producer_:
   - Some of the glucose produced in photosynthesis is used in respiration, but _not_ for _growth_.

   ② Energy from plant respiration not used for growth

3) Energy is lost _between_ the producer and primary consumer:
   - _Some parts_ of the producers _aren't eaten_, e.g. the roots.
   - Consumers _can't digest_ (so can't get energy from) all of the material they eat, e.g. tree bark. The energy is lost as _waste_, e.g. in faeces.

   ③ Non-edible and non-digestable parts

4) Energy is _lost_ from the _primary consumer_:
   - Some of the energy from respiration is _not_ used for _growth_, e.g. it's used for _movement_ and to _keep warm_.

   ④ Movement and keeping warm

5) Energy is lost _between_ the primary consumer and secondary consumer:
   - _Some parts_ of the consumers _aren't eaten_, e.g. the bones.
   - Consumers _can't digest_ (so can't get energy from) all of the material they eat, e.g. fur. The energy is lost as _waste_, e.g. in faeces.

   ⑤ Non-edible and non-digestable parts

See if you can answer these questions:

1) What is an ecosystem?
2) What does a food chain show?
3) What do secondary consumers eat?
4) Give two ways energy is lost in food chains.

Answers
1) All the organisms in a place and all the non-living factors that are there.
2) Which organisms eat which others / one way the energy is passed from a producer to the last consumer.
3) Primary consumers (herbivores).
4) Energy from plant respiration not used for growth / Energy from animal respiration not used for growth, e.g. used for movement and warmth / Lost in uneaten material / Lost in undigested material/waste.

Ecological Pyramids

Ecological Pyramids can Show Numbers, Mass or Energy

1) <u>Ecological pyramids</u> show something about each level of a food chain. They either show the <u>number</u> of organisms, the <u>mass</u> of organisms or the <u>energy</u> in the organisms.
2) Each <u>block</u> (rectangle) in the pyramid shows a <u>different trophic level</u> — the <u>bottom block</u> is the <u>first level</u> (<u>producer</u>), the next block is the <u>second</u> level (<u>primary consumer</u>), the <u>third</u> block is the third level (<u>secondary consumer</u>) and so on...
3) The <u>size</u> of the block represents the <u>size</u> of that level.

Pyramids of Numbers Show the Number of Organisms

1) A <u>large block</u> means there are a <u>large number</u> of individual organisms at that level. For example:

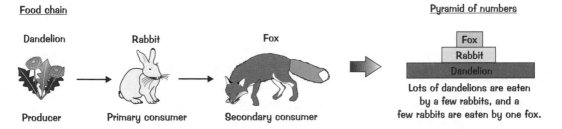

2) Pyramids of numbers are <u>often not pyramid shaped</u> — this is because each individual organism is counted as <u>one unit</u> regardless of <u>size</u>, e.g. a small caterpillar and a huge oak tree are both just one unit:

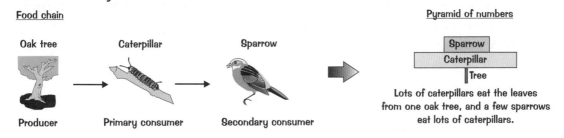

The Blocks in Pyramids of Biomass show the Total Mass

<u>Pyramids of biomass</u> show the <u>total dry mass</u> of organisms at each trophic level. Each block represent the <u>mass</u> of organisms <u>per unit area or volume</u>, e.g. grams per square metre (g m^{-2}) or grams per cubic metre (g m^{-3}).

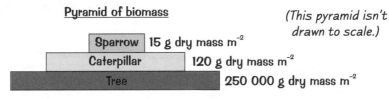

Pyramids of biomass are created by taking a <u>sample</u> (small number) of organisms from each trophic level, finding their dry mass, and <u>multiplying</u> it by the <u>total population size</u> to get the <u>total mass</u> in the whole trophic level. So the biomass at <u>a given moment</u> is counted. Because they only show the biomass at any one moment, pyramids of biomass can sometimes be a bit <u>misleading</u> — check out the next page to see why...

Ecological Pyramids

Pyramids of Biomass Have Their faults

1) Because pyramids of biomass only give the <u>amount of biomass at any one moment</u> they don't show the <u>rate of production</u> of biomass — the <u>productivity</u> (how quickly things at that trophic level <u>grow</u>).

2) If the organisms at one level are being <u>eaten</u> as fast as they're being <u>produced</u>, the amount of biomass at any one time might be <u>small</u> but a <u>large</u> amount of biomass is actually being created and eaten by the next level every year.

3) For example, a <u>grazed field</u> has a relatively <u>small</u> amount of <u>biomass</u> at <u>any one time</u>, but the <u>amount of biomass being produced and eaten</u> each year from the grazed field is actually quite <u>large</u>.

Pyramids of Energy are the Most Useful Pyramids to Use

1) <u>Pyramids of energy</u> show the <u>amount of energy</u> in <u>each trophic level</u> over a <u>given period of time</u>.

2) This means that pyramids of energy <u>do</u> show the <u>rate of production</u> of biomass.

3) Examples of units that are used include: <u>kilojoules per square metre per year</u> ($kJ \ m^{-2} \ yr^{-1}$) and <u>kilojoules per cubic metre per year</u> ($kJ \ m^{-3} \ yr^{-1}$).

4) Energy is <u>lost</u> at each trophic level (see page 6) — the amount of energy <u>decreases</u> as you <u>move up</u> the pyramid from the <u>producers</u> (bottom block). This means that pyramids of energy are <u>always pyramid shaped</u>.

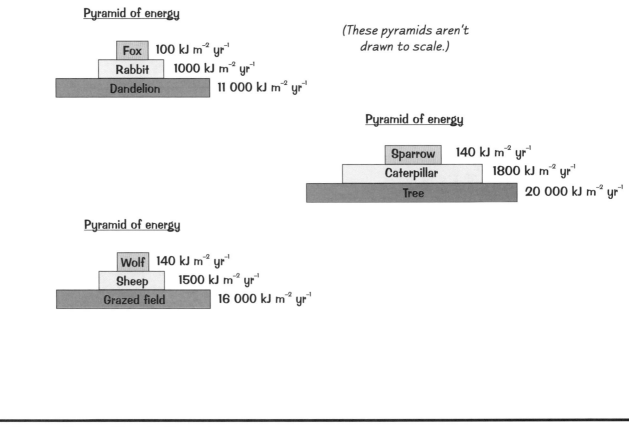

Pyramid of energy

Fox	100 $kJ \ m^{-2} \ yr^{-1}$
Rabbit	1000 $kJ \ m^{-2} \ yr^{-1}$
Dandelion	11 000 $kJ \ m^{-2} \ yr^{-1}$

(These pyramids aren't drawn to scale.)

Pyramid of energy

Sparrow	140 $kJ \ m^{-2} \ yr^{-1}$
Caterpillar	1800 $kJ \ m^{-2} \ yr^{-1}$
Tree	20 000 $kJ \ m^{-2} \ yr^{-1}$

Pyramid of energy

Wolf	140 $kJ \ m^{-2} \ yr^{-1}$
Sheep	1500 $kJ \ m^{-2} \ yr^{-1}$
Grazed field	16 000 $kJ \ m^{-2} \ yr^{-1}$

Ecological Pyramids and Energy Flow

You can Calculate How Efficient the Flow of Energy Is

Pyramids of energy give the <u>amount of energy</u> present at each trophic level. This also shows the <u>total</u> amount of energy that's <u>available</u> to the next level. But as you learnt earlier, lots of energy gets lost, so not all of the available energy moves onto the next level. You can <u>calculate</u> how much energy is <u>lost</u> between each level by doing some simple sums. You can also calculate how <u>efficient</u> (how much is passed on as a <u>percentage</u> of the energy available) the energy flow between each level is:

1) There's 11 000 kJ m^{-2} yr^{-1} of energy in the <u>dandelions</u>, so 11 000 kJ m^{-2} yr^{-1} of energy is <u>available</u> to the next level — the rabbits.

<u>Pyramid of energy</u>

Fox	100 kJ m^{-2} yr^{-1}
Rabbit	1000 kJ m^{-2} yr^{-1}
Dandelion	11 000 kJ m^{-2} yr^{-1}

2) But there's only 1000 kJ m^{-2} yr^{-1} of energy in the rabbits, so you can calculate how much energy has been <u>lost between</u> the levels:

loss = energy that was available to the level – energy in the level
loss = 11 000 – 1000 = 10 000 kJ m^{-2} yr^{-1}

3) You can calculate how <u>efficient</u> the flow (<u>transfer</u>) of energy between these two levels has been:

$$\text{efficiency} = \frac{\text{energy in a level}}{\text{energy that was available to the level}} \times 100$$

efficiency of energy transfer from dandelions to rabbits

$$= \frac{1000}{11\,000} \times 100 = \underline{9.1\,\%}$$

> You can do these calculations for <u>energy transfer between any</u> of the levels.

Three whole pages without any questions? No chance:

1) What do pyramids of numbers show?
2) Draw a rough pyramid of numbers for the following food chain: grass → hedgehog → fleas
3) What do pyramids of biomass show?
4) What do pyramids of energy show?
5) Use the following food chain to answer questions a) to c):
   Oak tree (82 000 kJ m^{-2} yr^{-1}) → Beetle (5900 kJ m^{-2} yr^{-1}) → Woodpecker (560 kJ m^{-2} yr^{-1})
   a) Draw and label a pyramid of energy for the food chain.
   b) Calculate the amount of energy lost between the producers and primary consumers.
   c) Calculate the efficiency of energy transfer between the primary and secondary consumers.

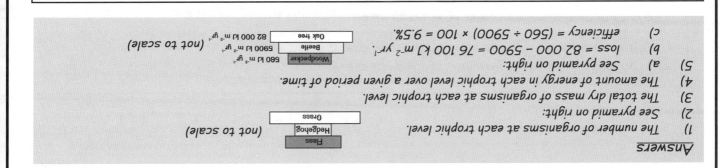

Answers

1) The number of organisms at each trophic level.
2) See pyramid on right:
3) The total dry mass of organisms at each trophic level.
4) The amount of energy in each trophic level over a given period of time.
5) a) See pyramid on right:
   b) loss = 82 000 – 5900 = 76 100 kJ m^{-2} yr^{-1}.
   c) efficiency = (560 ÷ 5900) × 100 = 9.5%.

Fleas	
Hedgehog	(not to scale)
Grass	

Woodpecker	560 kJ m^{-2} yr^{-1}
Beetle	5900 kJ m^{-2} yr^{-1} (not to scale)
Oak tree	82 000 kJ m^{-2} yr^{-1}

Farming and Energy Flow

Productivity is Basically Growth

1) When <u>farmers</u> grow crops or animals for <u>food</u> they want them to be as <u>productive</u> as possible — basically this means they want them to <u>grow as much as possible</u> in <u>as little time as possible</u>.

2) Farmers can <u>manipulate</u> the <u>flow of energy</u> in <u>food chains</u> so that as <u>little energy</u> as possible is <u>lost</u> and as <u>much energy</u> as possible is used by their crops and animals for <u>growth</u>.

3) This <u>increases</u> the <u>efficiency of energy transfer</u> (the amount of energy that's passed on to the next trophic level), which increases the amount of energy for <u>growth</u>, increasing <u>productivity</u>.

Farmers Increase Productivity In Many Ways

Farmers <u>increase</u> the efficiency of energy transfer (and so productivity), by looking at all the ways energy is <u>lost</u> in a food chain and <u>stopping or reducing</u> that energy loss. For example:

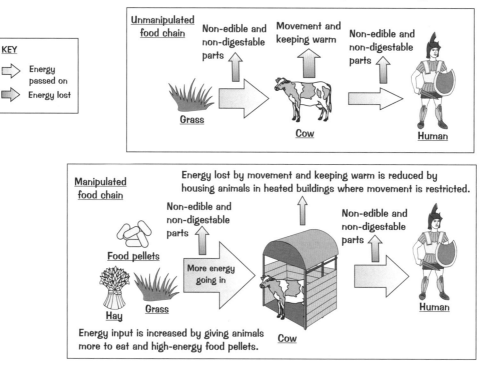

Farmers increase productivity in <u>crops</u> by:

1) Using <u>pesticides</u> to kill pests that normally <u>eat crops</u> (and so reduce productivity).

2) Using <u>herbicides</u> to kill weeds that <u>compete</u> with crops for factors needed for <u>growth</u>.

3) Applying <u>fertilisers</u> that provide crops with more of the factors that are needed for growth.

Two juicy little questions to get your teeth into:

1) Why do farmers want to manipulate food chains?

2) Suggest two ways a farmer could reduce energy loss.

Answers

1) To increase productivity.

2) House animals in heated/small buildings to reduce energy lost through heat/movement / use pesticides to kill pests that eat crops.

Factors Affecting Population Size

Population Sizes are Limited by Various Factors

A _population_ is a _group_ of organisms of the _same species_ living in a _certain area_.
Population _size_ is the _number_ of organisms in the population. Population size is _limited_ because
the different resources needed for _survival_ are limited. These resources include:

1) The amount of _food_ and _minerals_ available.
2) The amount of _water_ in the area.
3) How much _shelter_ there is and how good the shelter is.
4) How much _light's_ available (usually for plants).

For example, if a hot and wet summer means _plenty_ of food is available in an area,
the population will _increase_ as more individuals _can survive_ there — more individuals
may _move_ to the area or individuals already there may have _more offspring_ (children).
If bad weather (e.g. _drought_) means there's _little food_ available, _fewer_ individuals can
survive so the population _decreases_ — individuals may move to new areas (where there's
more food) or individuals already there may have _fewer offspring_ or _die_.

Individuals Compete for Resources

Because resources like food are limited, individuals have to _compete_ with each other for them.
There are _two_ different types of competition:

1) Competition between individuals of the _same_ species — called int_ra_specific competition.
   E.g. how _you_ and your _brother_ fight (compete) for the remote control.
2) Competition between individuals of _different_ species — called int_er_specific competition.
   E.g. how _you_ and the family _cat_ compete for the comfiest chair.

Predation also Affects Population Size

Most ecosystems contain _prey_ (organisms that are _eaten_) and _predators_ (organisms that do
the _eating_). Because prey are a _food source_, the prey's population size affects the predator's
population size. But the opposite is also true — the predator's population size affects the prey's
population size. The population sizes of predators and their prey go _up and down in cycles_.

E.g. if there's a _large_ population of rabbits in an area, there's _plenty_
of food for _foxes_, so the population size of _foxes_ will _increase_.
This means _more rabbits_ will be _eaten_, so the population size
of _rabbits_ will _decrease_. There's now less food available for the foxes,
so the population of foxes decreases and so on...

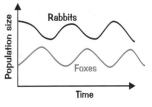

See if you can answer these questions:

1) Give two resources that limit population size.
2) When mice compete with other mice for resources, what kind of competition is this?
3) When mice compete with rats for resources, what kind of competition is this?

The Carbon Cycle

Bacteria and Fungi are Decomposers

Living organisms need large quantities of carbon, hydrogen, oxygen, nitrogen and sulfur, among other things. These elements are constantly being <u>recycled</u> through ecosystems — they're recycled between plants, animals and the atmosphere. Luckily for you, you only need to concentrate on the <u>carbon</u> and <u>nitrogen cycle</u>. <u>Bacteria and fungi</u> play an important role in the recycling of carbon and nitrogen:

1) <u>Organic compounds</u> (compounds that contain <u>carbon</u>) and <u>nitrogen-containing</u> compounds in <u>dead organisms</u> and <u>faeces</u> are <u>broken down</u> by microorganisms (bacteria and fungi). This is called <u>decomposition</u>.

2) Bacteria and fungi do this by releasing <u>digestive enzymes</u> onto the organic material and then <u>absorbing</u> the products of digestion. This method of feeding is called <u>saprobiontic nutrition</u>.

The Carbon Cycle Involves Many Different Processes

<u>All organisms</u> need <u>carbon</u> to make <u>organic compounds</u>, e.g. carbohydrates, proteins and lipids. Carbon is <u>removed</u> from the atmosphere during <u>photosynthesis</u>. It's <u>released back</u> into the atmosphere as <u>carbon dioxide</u> (CO_2) by <u>respiration</u> and <u>combustion</u> during the <u>carbon cycle</u>:

1) Carbon in CO_2 in the <u>atmosphere</u> enters plants (<u>producers</u>) by <u>photosynthesis</u>.

2) Some of the carbon stays in the plant tissues as organic compounds, but some is <u>released</u> when CO_2 is <u>produced</u> during plant <u>respiration</u>.

3) Carbon passes <u>along food chains</u> as <u>primary consumers</u> eat plant tissues and <u>secondary consumers</u> etc eat other organisms.

4) Some carbon stays in the animals' tissues but some is <u>released</u> during <u>respiration</u>.

5) Carbon passes into <u>decomposers</u> as they break down and digest <u>dead organisms</u> (including other decomposers) and <u>faeces</u>. Some carbon stays in the microorganisms and some is <u>released</u> when they <u>respire</u> too.

6) If organisms die where there <u>aren't any decomposers</u>, they aren't decomposed and the carbon stays <u>locked</u> in their <u>remains</u>. Over millions of years, the remains of the organisms change into <u>fossil fuels</u> such as <u>coal</u>, <u>oil</u> and <u>gas</u>. <u>Burning</u> these fuels (combustion) <u>releases</u> the carbon in to the atmosphere as CO_2.

7) Forests contain a large amount of carbon <u>locked up</u> in the organisms as organic compounds — so forests are called <u>carbon sinks</u>. If forests are <u>burnt down</u> the stored CO_2 is released back into the atmosphere.

The carbon cycle:

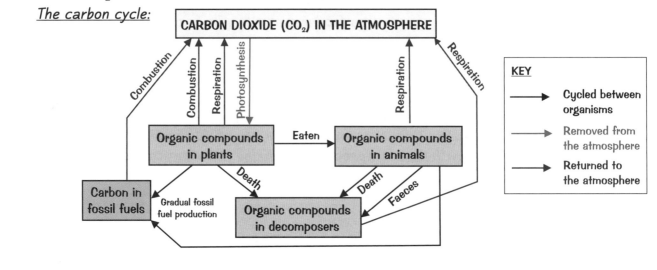

The Nitrogen Cycle

The Nitrogen Cycle Involves Four Different Processes

All organisms need nitrogen to make nitrogen compounds, e.g. proteins and nucleic acids. Nitrogen is recycled through plants, animals and the atmosphere during the nitrogen cycle. Nitrogen gas can only be removed from the atmosphere by a few nitrogen-fixing bacteria — they convert the nitrogen gas into biologically useful forms. Because only a few types of bacteria can do this, nitrogen is often in short supply in ecosystems. Nitrogen is returned to the atmosphere by other bacteria (denitrifying bacteria) when they respire:

1) Nitrogen, from nitrogen gas in the atmosphere, enters the nitrogen cycle by the process of nitrogen fixation. Bacteria in the soil convert nitrogen gas into nitrogen compounds that can be used by plants.

2) Plants absorb the nitrogen compounds and use them to make proteins and nucleic acids.

3) Nitrogen passes along food chains as organisms are eaten.

4) Decomposers turn the nitrogen compounds from dead organisms (including other decomposers), faeces and urine into ammonium compounds. This process is called ammonification.

5) The ammonium compounds are then turned into nitrites and then into nitrates by nitrifying bacteria — this is called nitrification.

6) Dentrifying bacteria use the nitrates in the soil to carry out respiration, which releases nitrogen gas back into the atmosphere. This process is called denitrification.

The nitrogen cycle:

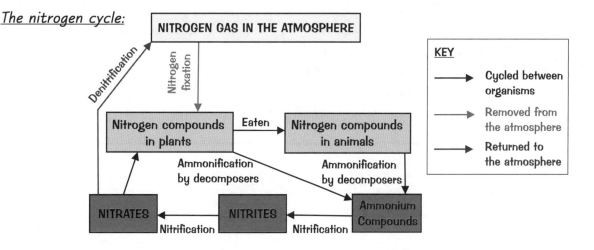

Not Many Plants Grow Well in Waterlogged Soil

Nitrifying bacteria need oxygen to make nitrates. Waterlogged ground has very little oxygen in it, so nitrifying bacteria can't make nitrates. Nitrates are needed by plants to make amino acids for growth. So plants find it hard to grow in waterlogged ground because of the lack of nitrates.

Also, denitrifying bacteria use nitrates and nitrites when they respire, releasing nitrogen gas into the atmosphere, reducing the amount of nitrates in the soil.

Test Your Understanding

A whole page of questions on nutrient cycles. What a treat:

1) What types of microorganisms are decomposers?
2) What is an organic compound?
3) Name two types of organic compound.
4) Which process removes carbon dioxide from the atmosphere?
5) Name the process of burning fossil fuels.
6) Forests are carbon sinks.
   a) What does this mean?
   b) How does burning wood from forests affect the carbon cycle?
7) Use the carbon cycle diagram on the right to answer the following questions:
   a) Name the process labelled A.
   b) Name the process labelled B.
   c) What does C represent?
8) Name two types of nitrogen compound.
9) Outline the steps involved in nitrification.
10) What are denitrifying bacteria?
11) Use the nitrogen cycle diagram on the right to answer the following questions:
    a) Name the process labelled A.
    b) Name the type of microorganism involved in the process labelled B.
    c) Name the compounds labelled C.
12) Explain why most plants find it hard to grow in waterlogged soil.

CARBON DIOXIDE — Carbon in plants — Eaten — Carbon in animals — C — Carbon in decomposers (labels A and B)

NITROGEN GAS — A — Proteins in plants — Eaten — Proteins in animals — NITRATES — C — Ammonium Compounds (labels B)

Answers

1) Fungi and bacteria.
2) A compound that contains carbon.
3) E.g. carbohydrate / protein / lipid.
4) Photosynthesis.
5) Combustion.
6) a) It means forests contain a large amount of carbon locked up in organic compounds.
   b) The stored carbon is released into the atmosphere as CO_2.
7) a) Respiration.
   b) Combustion.
   c) Fossil fuels.
8) E.g. proteins and nucleic acids.
9) Ammonium compounds are turned into nitrites and then nitrates by nitrifying bacteria.
10) Bacteria in soil that use nitrates for respiration, producing nitrogen gas that's released back into the atmosphere.
11) a) Nitrogen fixation.
    b) Nitrifying bacteria.
    c) Nitrites.
12) Plants need nitrates to grow. They get these nitrates from the soil. Nitrifying bacteria in the soil need oxygen to make nitrates. Waterlogged ground has very little oxygen, so little nitrate is produced.

Global Warming

Global Warming is the Recent Rise in Global Temperature

1) <u>Global warming</u> is the term that's used to describe the <u>rapid increase</u> in <u>average global temperature</u> in the <u>last century</u>.

2) During the same period, the <u>atmospheric concentration of carbon dioxide</u> (CO_2) has <u>rapidly increased too</u>.

3) <u>Most scientists</u> think that these two things are <u>linked</u>. And most scientists think that the recent rapid rise in CO_2 has been mostly caused by <u>human activity</u>, e.g. burning fossil fuels.

4) Both temperature and carbon dioxide concentration have <u>increased</u> — no one <u>disagrees</u> about that. But some people <u>don't think</u> there's a link between the two, and other people <u>do think</u> there's a link, but that the increase in CO_2 <u>isn't</u> caused by <u>human activity</u> — it's a natural <u>rise</u> (like <u>past</u> rises and falls).

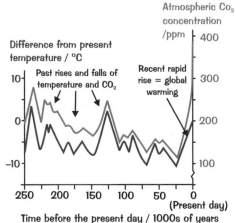

Increasing CO_2 is Enhancing the Greenhouse Effect

1) The <u>Earth</u> is <u>heated</u> by energy from the <u>Sun</u>.

2) <u>Greenhouse gases</u>, like <u>CO_2</u> and <u>methane</u>, surround the Earth and create a kind of <u>blanket</u> that absorbs some Sunlight energy reflected from the Earth and <u>stops</u> it being <u>released</u> back into space.

3) Greenhouse gases help to keep the <u>Earth warm</u> by <u>re-radiating</u> the heat back down towards the Earth.

4) But if there's too much greenhouse gas, <u>too much</u> heat is absorbed and not enough is released into space, so the Earth gets <u>warmer</u>.

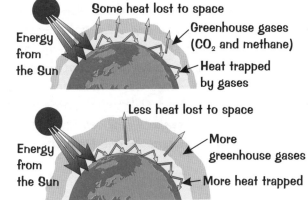

Global Warming is a Type of Climate Change

<u>Climate change</u> is any <u>big</u> change in the <u>weather</u> of an area over at least <u>several decades</u>, e.g. a change in average <u>temperature</u> or a change in average <u>rainfall</u>. This means that global warming is a <u>type</u> of climate change. Global warming is also thought to be <u>causing</u> other types of climate change — e.g. periods of <u>reduced rainfall</u> (leading to drought) in some areas, but <u>increased rainfall</u> (leading to flooding) in other areas.

Only two questions this time:

1) What is global warming?
2) Name two greenhouse gases.

Genes and Alleles

Humans have Two Alleles of Each Gene

1) Genes are sections of DNA that contain the instructions to make proteins. These proteins control what characteristics you have. So your genes determine your characteristics.

2) Alleles are different versions of genes — they have slightly different DNA sequences from each other and so create slightly different proteins and slightly different versions of the characteristic. For example, different alleles of the gene for eye colour control whether your eyes are blue or brown.

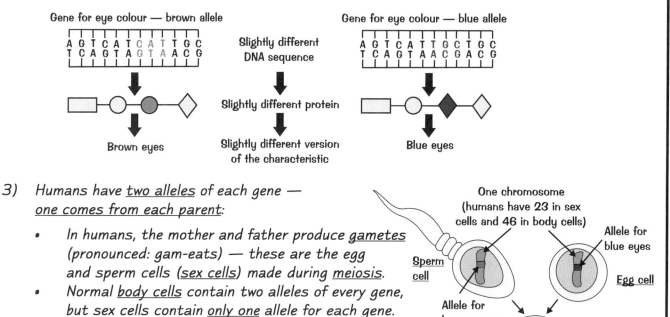

3) Humans have two alleles of each gene — one comes from each parent:

• In humans, the mother and father produce gametes (pronounced: gam-eats) — these are the egg and sperm cells (sex cells) made during meiosis.

• Normal body cells contain two alleles of every gene, but sex cells contain only one allele for each gene.

• During fertilisation, an egg and a sperm come together to create a new cell (zygote), which now has two alleles of each gene — one from the mother and one from the father.

Get Your Head Round these Terms

1) Phenotype (pronounced like this: feen-o-type) — what characteristics a person has, e.g. brown eyes.

2) Genotype — what alleles a person has, e.g. two alleles for brown eyes.

3) Dominant allele — an allele whose characteristic appears in the phenotype even when there's only one copy, e.g. the brown eye allele is dominant over the blue eye allele, so if you have one brown allele and one blue allele your eyes will be brown. Dominant alleles are shown using capital letters, e.g. B for the brown eye allele.

4) Recessive allele — an allele whose characteristic only appears in the phenotype if two copies are present, e.g. the blue eye allele is recessive to the brown eye allele, so your eyes will only be blue if you have two blue alleles. Recessive alleles are shown using lower case letters, e.g. b for the blue allele.

5) Homozygous — if a person has two copies of the same allele then they are said to be homozygous, e.g. BB is homozygous for brown eyes.

6) Heterozygous — if a person has two different alleles then they are said to be heterozygous, e.g. Bb is heterozygous for brown eyes.

Homo means the same. Hetero means different.

Genetic Diagrams

Work Out Offspring Phenotypes Using Genetic Diagrams

1) Sometimes you want to know what _phenotype_ (characteristics) the _offspring_ (children) of two parents might have.

2) Usually, all you know is the genotype of the two parents.

3) You have to use a _genetic diagram_ to work out the phenotypes of the offspring:

   a) First you figure out what alleles the _parents' gametes could have_.

   b) Then you figure out _all the different ways_ the parents' gametes (and so their alleles) could come together.

   c) And from this you know _what alleles_ (i.e. genotype) any _possible offspring_ might have. Which means you can work out what _phenotypes_ they would have.

> When two organisms are _crossed_ it means they're _bred together_ to make offspring

For example, say you want to cross a father with genotype _bb_ for eye colour and a mother with genotype _Bb_ for eye colour:

a) Work out what alleles the parents' gametes could have — each gamete can _only have one_ of two alleles, so _draw two circles_ with _one allele in each_. It can help to use _colour_, e.g. _black_ for dominant, _blue_ for recessive.

b) Then work out all the _possible ways_ these gametes and their alleles could come together — do this in _stages_:

   1) The four gametes could come together in _four different ways_, so draw four circles.

   2) Draw _arrows_ showing where the _father's alleles go_ first.

   3) Then _draw arrows_ showing where the _mother's alleles go_.

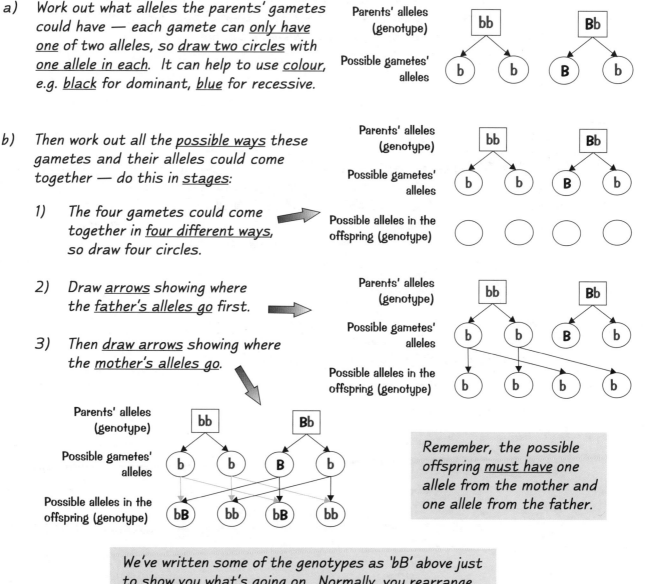

> Remember, the possible offspring _must have_ one allele from the mother and one allele from the father.

> We've written some of the genotypes as 'bB' above just to show you what's going on. Normally, you rearrange the letters so the capital letter comes first, e.g. 'Bb'.

Genetic Diagrams

c) *Now you know what alleles (and so what genotypes) any possible offspring could have — there's a 50% chance they'll have bB and a 50% chance they'll have bb. This can also be written as a* *<u>1 : 1 ratio</u>* *of* *<u>bB : bb</u>*.

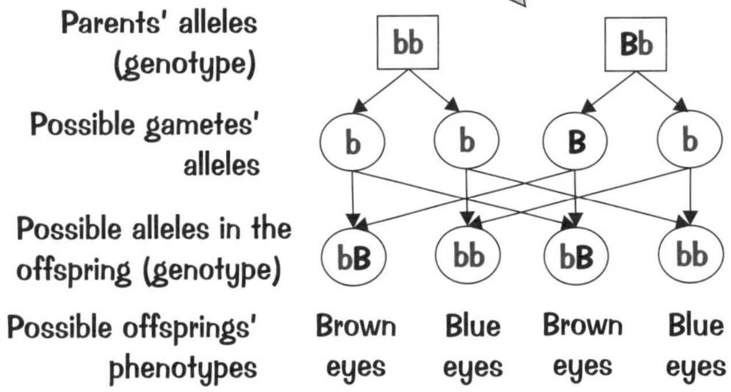

You can also work out the <u>phenotypes</u> of the possible offspring, as you know which allele is <u>dominant</u> and which is <u>recessive</u>: B is dominant so BB and Bb are brown, and bb is blue. So there's a <u>50%</u> chance any offspring will have blue eyes and a 50% chance they'll have brown eyes, or there's a <u>1 : 1 ratio</u> of <u>blue : brown eyes</u>.

Sometimes you might only be told the <u>phenotype</u> of the parents — so to do a genetic diagram you have to <u>work out</u> the <u>genotype</u>, e.g. <u>homozygous</u> for brown eyes would be BB, <u>heterozygous</u> for brown eyes would be Bb.

See if you can answer these questions:

1) *What are alleles?*
2) *Is the allele 'Q' dominant or recessive?*
3) *If a person has the alleles Rr, are they heterozygous or homozygous?*
4) *Fingernail colour in native British giraffes has two alleles — N for navy and n for white.*
   a) *Complete the picture on the right to show the parents' alleles and gametes' alleles for a cross between a homozygous navy parent and a heterozygous navy parent.*
   b) *Complete the genetic diagram for this cross and use it to answer the following question: what percentage of possible offspring will have navy fingernails?*

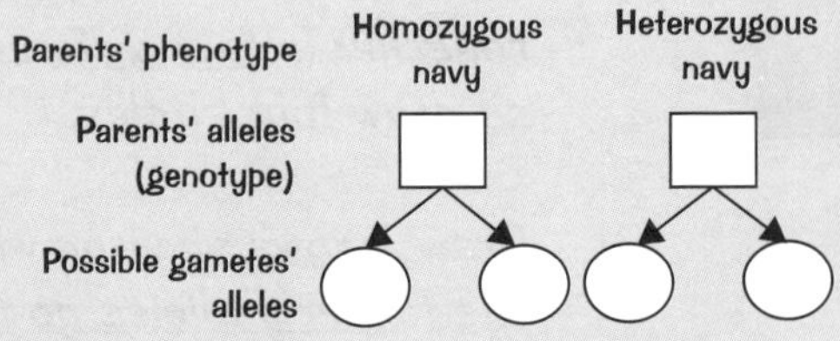

Answers

1) *Alleles are different versions of a gene (they have slightly different DNA sequences from each other).*
2) *Dominant (it's a capital letter).*
3) *Heterozygous (they have two different alleles).*
4) *a)*

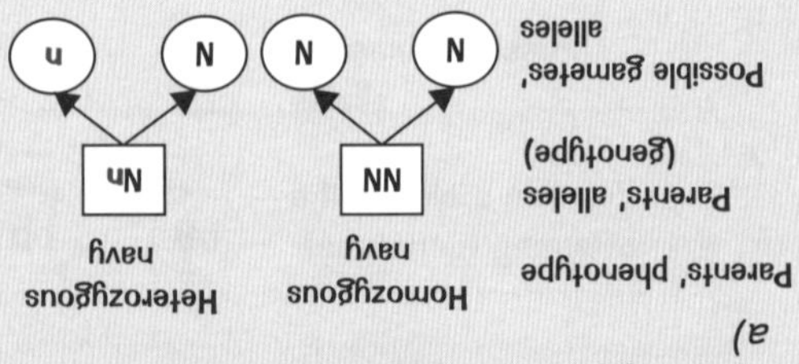

b)

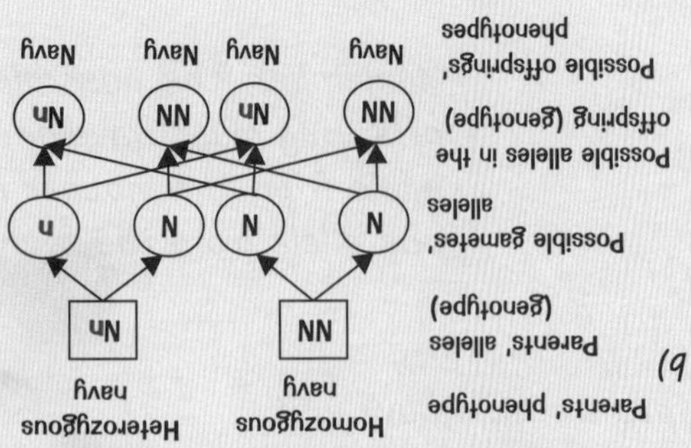

100% of offspring will have navy fingernails

Genetic Diagrams

Genetic Diagrams can Also be Drawn as Punnett Squares

For example, if you do the same cross as on page 17 — a father with genotype _bb_ for eye colour and a mother with genotype _Bb_ for eye colour:

a) The first step is the same — work out what alleles the parents' gametes could have, then <u>draw two circles</u> with <u>one allele in each</u>.

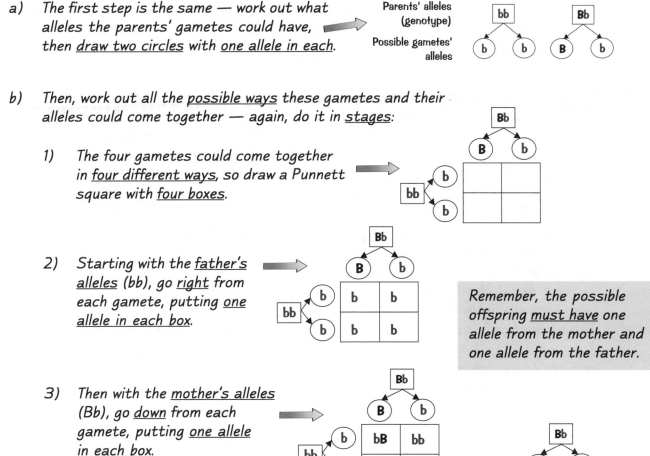

b) Then, work out all the <u>possible ways</u> these gametes and their alleles could come together — again, do it in <u>stages</u>:

1) The four gametes could come together in <u>four different ways</u>, so draw a Punnett square with <u>four boxes</u>.

2) Starting with the <u>father's</u> alleles (bb), go <u>right</u> from each gamete, putting <u>one allele in each box</u>.

> Remember, the possible offspring <u>must have</u> one allele from the mother and one allele from the father.

3) Then with the <u>mother's alleles</u> (Bb), go <u>down</u> from each gamete, putting <u>one allele in each box</u>.

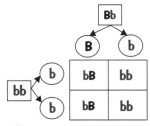

c) Finally, you can work out the <u>phenotypes</u> of the possible offspring: B is dominant so BB and Bb are brown and bb is blue. So there's a <u>50%</u> chance any offspring will have blue eyes and a 50% chance they'll have brown eyes. This can also be written as a <u>1 : 1 ratio</u> of <u>brown : blue eyes</u>.

Offspring:
Two **bB** genotypes, so two offspring with brown eyes. Two **bb** genotypes, so two offspring with blue eyes.

Have a go at this question.

1) Mouse fur colour is controlled by a dominant grey allele (G) and a recessive black allele (g).
   a) What are the genotypes of a homozygous grey coated parent and a homozygous black coated parent?
   b) Draw a Punnett square to show the cross of these two parents.

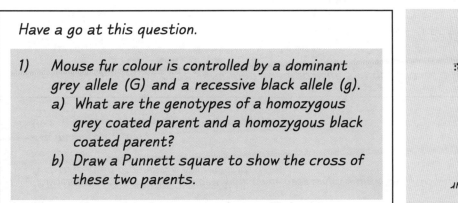

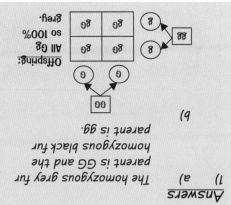

Answers
1) a) The homozygous grey fur parent is GG and the homozygous black fur parent is gg.
b) Offspring: All Gg so 100% grey.

Responding to the Environment

Responding to the Environment Increases Survival

1) Organisms need to respond to <u>changes</u> in their <u>external environment</u>,
   e.g. to the presence of predators or food.

2) They also need to respond to <u>changes</u> in their <u>internal environment</u> (inside their bodies),
   e.g. a drop in blood glucose concentration or an increase in body temperature.

3) Responding to changes <u>increases an organism's chance of survival</u>
   — if they didn't respond to these things they'd die.

A Change in an Organism's Environment is a Stimulus

1) <u>Stimuli</u> (changes) are <u>detected</u> by <u>receptors</u> in the body.

2) The <u>information</u> is then <u>communicated</u> (sent) to an <u>effector</u>
   — something that causes a <u>response</u>.

3) Effectors include <u>muscles</u> and <u>glands</u>:
   a) <u>Muscle cells</u> can respond in <u>different ways</u>,
      e.g. muscles in the eye <u>contract</u> to make the pupil
      smaller, and muscle cells can <u>take up glucose</u>.
   b) <u>Gland cells</u> can also respond in different ways,
      e.g. sweat glands <u>secrete</u> sweat to cool the body down,
      and cells in the liver (a gland) can also <u>take up glucose</u>.

> The <u>plural</u>
> of stimulus
> is <u>stimuli</u>.

4) The information is communicated by the <u>nervous system</u> (along <u>neurones</u>) or by the
   <u>hormonal system</u> (using <u>hormones</u>). The nervous system and hormonal system are
   referred to as <u>communication systems</u>.

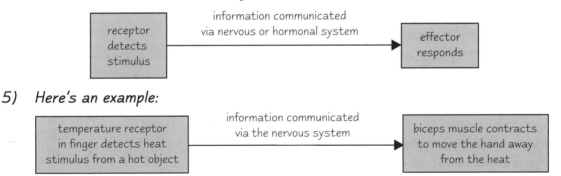

5) Here's an example:

See if you can answer these questions:

1) Why do organisms need to respond to their environment?
2) What is a stimulus?
3) What are stimuli detected by?
4) Give one type of effector.
5) How is information about an organism's environment communicated to effectors?

Answers
1) To increase their chances of survival.
2) A change in an organism's environment.
3) Receptors.
4) E.g. muscles / glands.
5) By the nervous system or the hormonal system.

The Nervous System

Nervous System Receptors Trigger Nerve Impulses

1) *Different receptors* detect *different stimuli*, e.g. light receptors in the eye detect light and pressure receptors in the skin detect pressure (touch).

2) The receptors are connected to a *neurone* (nerve cell) and when they're stimulated they *trigger* a *nerve impulse*.

Nerve Impulses Travel Along Neurones to Effectors

1) *Sensory neurones* carry information from receptors *to* the *central nervous system* (CNS). (The central nervous system is made up of the *brain* and *spinal cord*.)

2) The CNS *processes* the information and *decides what to do* about it.

3) *Motor neurones* then carry the information from the CNS *to* the *effectors*.

4) Muscle cells *always contract* in response to a *nerve impulse*, and gland cells *always secrete* a substance.

brain
spinal cord

receptor detects stimulus and generates nerve impulse → sensory neurone → CNS → motor neurone → muscle contracts OR gland secretes substance

sensory and motor neurones

Nerve Impulses have to Cross Gaps Between Neurones

1) The nervous system is a *network* of billions of *neurones*.

2) *Information* may have to travel along *many neurones* to get from the receptor to the effector.

3) There are *tiny gaps* between the neurones called *synapses* (pronounced: sign-ap-ses).

4) When a nerve impulse reaches the end of a neurone it triggers the *release* of a *chemical* into the synapse.

5) The chemical *diffuses across* the gap, *binds* to *receptors* on the next neurone and triggers a *nerve impulse* in it.

6) So the information is passed across the synapse and carries on along its path.

chemical synapse
neurone neurone
nerve impulse

Reflex Responses Don't Involve Conscious Thought

1) Sometimes your body *responds* to a stimulus *without you deciding* how to respond.

2) These responses are called *reflex responses*.

3) The pathway of neurones that the information travels along is called a *reflex arc*.

4) In some reflexes the information travels along a sensory neurone, which *connects directly* to a *motor neurone* (causing a response). But usually another type of neurone is involved — a *relay neurone*. Relay neurones *connect sensory neurones to motor neurones*.

Reflex arc:

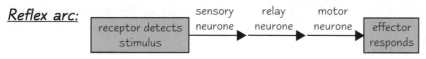

receptor detects stimulus → sensory neurone → relay neurone → motor neurone → effector responds

5) Reflexes are *faster* than normal responses because no time is spent *deciding* what the response should be.

The Hormonal System

Hormonal System Receptors Trigger Hormone Secretion

1) Hormonal system _receptors_ are _proteins_ on the _surface membranes_ of _cells_.
2) When they detect a stimulus they cause _hormones_ to be _secreted_.
3) Hormone secretion can also be _triggered_ by a _nerve impulse_.

Hormones Travel Around the Body in the Blood

1) Hormones are _transported_ around the body in the _blood_.
   This means hormonal responses are _slower_ than nervous system responses.
2) Hormones _only affect some cells_, called _target cells_.
3) This is because _only some cells_ have the _receptors_ for
   that hormone on their surface membrane.
4) When the hormone _binds_ to the receptors it causes a _response_.

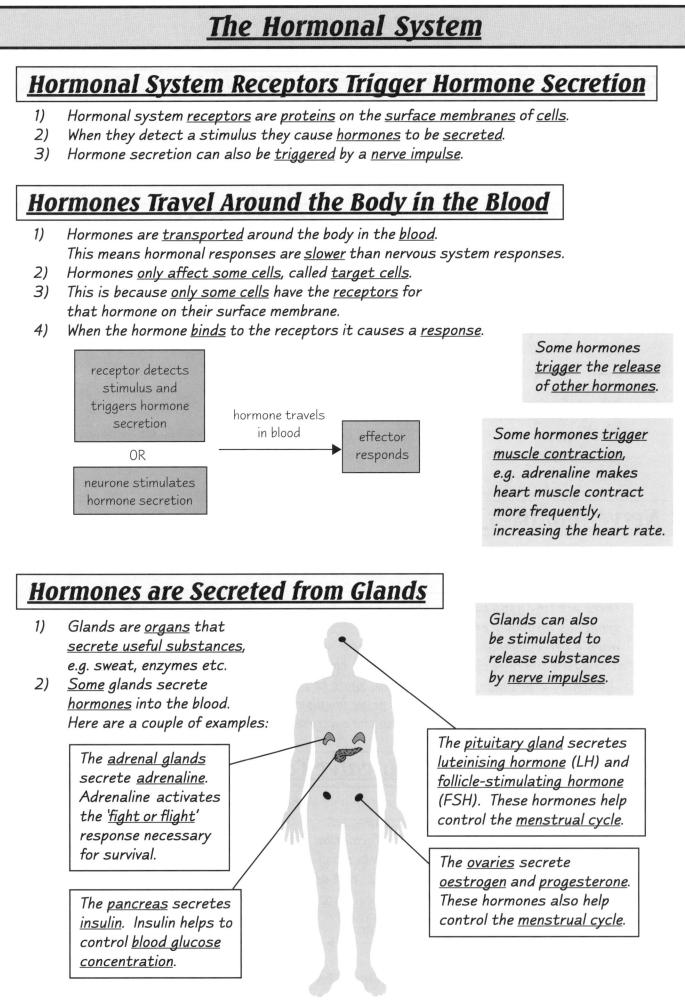

receptor detects stimulus and triggers hormone secretion

OR

neurone stimulates hormone secretion

hormone travels in blood

effector responds

Some hormones _trigger_ the _release_ of _other hormones_.

Some hormones _trigger muscle contraction_, e.g. adrenaline makes heart muscle contract more frequently, increasing the heart rate.

Hormones are Secreted from Glands

1) Glands are _organs_ that _secrete useful substances_, e.g. sweat, enzymes etc.
2) _Some_ glands secrete _hormones_ into the blood. Here are a couple of examples:

Glands can also be stimulated to release substances by _nerve impulses_.

The _adrenal glands_ secrete _adrenaline_. Adrenaline activates the 'fight or flight' response necessary for survival.

The _pancreas_ secretes _insulin_. Insulin helps to control _blood glucose concentration_.

The _pituitary gland_ secretes _luteinising hormone_ (LH) and _follicle-stimulating hormone_ (FSH). These hormones help control the _menstrual cycle_.

The _ovaries_ secrete _oestrogen_ and _progesterone_. These hormones also help control the _menstrual cycle_.

Test Your Understanding

Time to exercise your nervous system and answer these questions:

1) What happens when a nervous system receptor is stimulated?
2) Which type of neurones carry information from receptors to the CNS?
3) What is the role of the CNS in responding to stimuli?
4) Give the two possible responses of effectors to a nerve impulse.
5) What is the name of the gap between two neurones?
6) Describe how a nerve impulse crosses the gap between two neurones.
7) Draw a diagram of a reflex arc with three neurones.
   On the diagram label the sensory, relay and motor neurones, the receptor and the effector.
8) Describe two events that trigger the release of hormones.
9) How are hormones transported around the body?
10) Why do hormones only affect some cells?
11) What are glands?
12) Give two examples of hormones and state which glands they come from.
13) For the following three responses state the stimulus, communication system and effector:
   a) An increase in blood glucose concentration is detected by cells in the pancreas and triggers the pancreas to release insulin. Insulin causes liver cells to take up glucose.
   b) A decrease in blood pressure results in a nerve stimulating the heart muscle to contract more often.
   c) The smell of food is detected by receptors in the nose. This information is sent to the brain along neurones and results in the salivary glands secreting saliva.

Answers

1) A nerve impulse is triggered.
2) Sensory neurones.
3) The CNS processes the information from receptors and decides what to do about it.
4) Muscle cells contract and gland cells secrete substances.
5) A synapse.
6) When a nerve impulse reaches the end of a neurone it triggers the release of a chemical into the synapse. The chemical diffuses across the gap, binds to receptors on the next neurone and triggers a nerve impulse in it.
7)

receptor → sensory neurone → relay neurone → motor neurone → effector

8) A hormonal system receptor detecting a stimulus, and a nerve impulse.
9) In the blood.
10) Because only some cells have the receptors for that hormone on their surface membrane.
11) Organs that secrete useful substances.
12) E.g. adrenaline comes from the adrenal glands / insulin comes from the pancreas / oestrogen comes from the ovaries / progesterone comes from the ovaries / luteinising hormone (LH) comes from the pituitary gland / follicle-stimulating hormone (FSH) comes from the pituitary gland.
13) a) Stimulus — an increase in blood glucose concentration.
       Communication system — hormonal system (insulin is a hormone).
       Effector — liver cells (they respond by taking up glucose).
    b) Stimulus — a decrease in blood pressure.
       Communication system — nervous system (a nerve is involved).
       Effector — heart muscle cells.
    c) Stimulus — smell of food.
       Communication system — nervous system (the information is sent along neurones).
       Effector — salivary gland.

Homeostasis

Keeping Conditions Inside the Body Constant is Important

1) _Conditions inside_ the body (an organism's '_internal environment_') need to be _kept constant_. They need to be kept constant so the body _functions properly_ and _cells aren't damaged_.

2) Conditions that need to be kept constant include body temperature, blood glucose concentration, water content, blood pH and blood pressure.

3) The maintenance of a _constant internal environment_ is called _homeostasis_.

Negative Feedback Keeps Internal Conditions Constant

1) _Negative feedback mechanisms_ are _responses_ that bring a condition _back to normal_ when it's become too high or too low.

2) _Receptors_ detect when conditions have become _too high_ or _too low_.

3) The information is then _communicated to effectors_ by the _nervous system_ or the _hormonal system_ (or both). Which system's used depends on the condition being controlled.

Negative feedback mechanisms are sometimes called negative feedback loops.

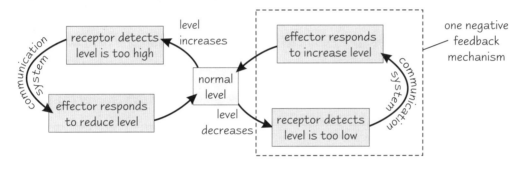

Blood Glucose Concentration is Controlled in Homeostasis

Blood glucose concentration has to be kept just right so that _cells have enough glucose_ for respiration, but so there isn't too much in the blood (which would cause water to leave cells by osmosis). As part of homeostasis it's controlled using negative feedback mechanisms:

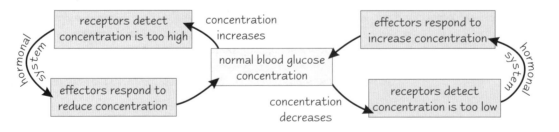

1) The _pancreas_ contains _receptors_ for glucose.

2) When they detect that the concentration is _too high_ they trigger the secretion of the hormone _insulin_.

3) Insulin acts on _muscle cells_ and _liver cells_ (the effectors) to _reduce_ the concentration of glucose in the blood.

4) When receptors in the pancreas detect that the concentration is _too low_ they trigger the secretion of another hormone called _glucagon_.

5) Glucagon acts on _liver cells_ (the effectors) to _increase_ the blood glucose concentration.

Insulin lowers blood glucose concentration.

Homeostasis

Body Temperature is Also Controlled in Homeostasis

Body temperature has to be kept constant so that _enzymes work efficiently_.
As part of homeostasis it's controlled using negative feedback mechanisms:

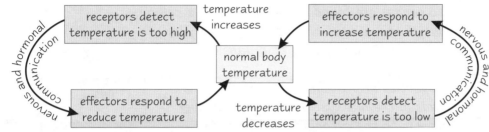

Control of body temperature is often called _thermoregulation_.

There are loads of responses that _reduce_ body temperature,
and loads that _increase_ body temperature:

Responses that REDUCE body temperature

- _Sweating more_ — heat is lost from the body when water in sweat _evaporates_. So the _more sweat_ produced, the _more heat is lost_.
- _Vasodilation_ — _arteries_ in the skin _dilate_ (widen) to allow more blood to flow in _capillaries_ at the _skin's surface_. This _increases_ the amount of _heat lost_ from the blood (and so from the body).
- _Hairs lie flat_ — mammals have hairs covering their bodies. When hairs _stand up_ they _trap a layer of air_ next to the body. Air is a _good thermal insulator_ (a thermal insulator is something that traps heat). So to _reduce body temperature_ hairs are made to _lie flat_ to trap as _little air_ (and so as _little heat_) as possible.

Responses that INCREASE body temperature

- _Sweating less_ — _less heat_ is _lost_ as there's less sweat produced.
- _Vasoconstriction_ — _arteries_ in the skin _constrict_ (get narrower) to reduce the amount of blood flowing in _capillaries_ at the _skin's surface_. This _reduces_ the amount of _heat lost_ from the blood.
- _Hairs stand up on end_ — this _traps a layer of air_, which _traps heat_ and _reduces_ the amount of _heat lost_.
- _Shivering_ — shivering is the rapid _contraction of muscles_. Muscle contraction _generates heat_, which increases body temperature.

Mammals sweat a little bit all the time. The amount of sweat produced is controlled to help keep body temperature constant.

Hairs standing up isn't really an important mechanism to increase body temperature in _humans_ as they don't have much hair. But it's pretty important in _other mammals_.

Have a go at these four questions:

1) Define homeostasis.
2) What is a negative feedback mechanism?
3) Which hormone reduces blood glucose concentration?
4) State four ways in which body temperature is increased.

Answers
1) Homeostasis is the maintenance of a constant internal environment.
2) A response that brings a condition back to normal when it's become too high or too low.
3) Insulin.
4) Sweating less / vasoconstriction / hairs stand up on end / shivering.

Section Six — Homeostasis

Protein Synthesis

DNA is Used to Make Proteins

1) <u>Genes</u> are <u>sections of DNA</u> that <u>code</u> (contain the <u>instructions</u>) for <u>proteins</u>.

2) DNA molecules (and so genes) are found in the <u>nucleus</u> of a cell but they can't move out of the nucleus because they're very <u>large</u>.

3) Protein synthesis happens in the <u>cytoplasm</u> at organelles called <u>ribosomes</u>.

4) So when a cell <u>needs</u> a particular protein, a <u>copy</u> of the gene that codes for it is made in the nucleus. This copy is <u>smaller</u> than DNA so it can move in to the cytoplasm, where it can be used to make the protein.

5) The copy of the gene is made from <u>RNA</u> (ribonucleic acid).

Protein synthesis just means making proteins.

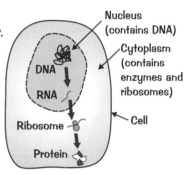

DNA is used as a Template to make RNA

1) The DNA in the gene acts as a <u>template</u>.

2) RNA and DNA <u>nucleotides</u> (the <u>units</u> RNA and DNA molecules are made up of) have parts called <u>bases</u>.

3) The bases on RNA nucleotides line up next to their <u>complementary</u> bases on the DNA template.

   • Complementary bases are bases that <u>complement</u> each other in <u>shape</u>, which means they can <u>bind</u> (stick) <u>together</u>. This is called <u>complementary base pairing or specific base pairing</u>.

   • In DNA, the bases adenine (A) and thymine (T) bind together, and so do the bases cytosine (C) and guanine (G). But in RNA, there's <u>no T</u>, so the base <u>uracil</u> (U) binds to any As in the DNA instead.

4) Eventually, a <u>whole copy</u> of the gene is made and the <u>sequence</u> (order) of <u>bases</u> in the RNA copy is complementary to the sequence of bases in the DNA template.

Complementary base pairs in DNA

Complementary base pairs in RNA

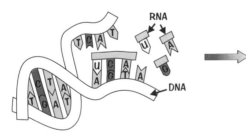

RNA U C A U U G A U C C
DNA A G T A A C T A G G

Try your luck with these questions:

1) Why does a copy of a gene need to be made for protein synthesis?

2) What is the copy of the gene made from?

3) Give the RNA sequence that would be complementary to the DNA sequence: ATTGCGCA

Answers

1) Because the DNA molecule containing the gene is in the nucleus and is too big to leave the nucleus. But protein synthesis takes place in the cytoplasm, so a copy of the gene that is smaller and can leave the nucleus needs to be made.

2) RNA.

3) UAACGCGU.

The Genetic Code and Mutations

The Order of Bases Determines the Order of Amino Acids

Three bases in a row (a _triplet_, e.g. GCT) codes for _one amino acid_ — this is called the _genetic code_. _Different amino acids_ are coded for by _different triplets_, e.g. TAT = tyrosine, AGT = serine. The _order of the bases_ (and so triplets) in the DNA of a gene determines the order of bases in its RNA copy, and that determines the _order of amino acids_ in a protein:

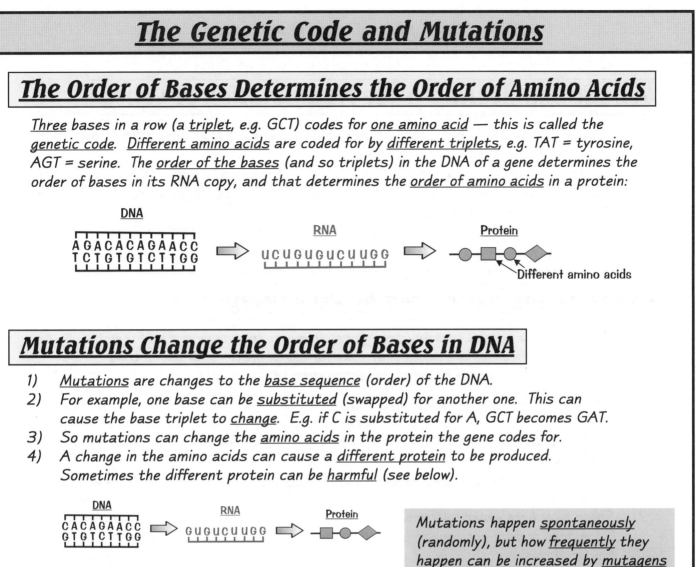

Mutations Change the Order of Bases in DNA

1) _Mutations_ are changes to the _base sequence_ (order) of the DNA.
2) For example, one base can be _substituted_ (swapped) for another one. This can cause the base triplet to _change_. E.g. if C is substituted for A, GCT becomes GAT.
3) So mutations can change the _amino acids_ in the protein the gene codes for.
4) A change in the amino acids can cause a _different protein_ to be produced. Sometimes the different protein can be _harmful_ (see below).

Mutations happen _spontaneously_ (randomly), but how _frequently_ they happen can be increased by _mutagens_ — factors that increase mutations, e.g. UV radiation in sunlight.

Mutations can be Harmful

Mutations can cause _cancer_ because _cell division_ is controlled by _proteins_. If mutations occur in the _genes_ for these proteins, they can _alter_ the proteins so they _no longer work_. This can lead to _uncontrolled cell division_, and the development of a _tumour_ (cancer).

Mutations also cause _genetic disorders_ — mutations that result in _altered_ genes and proteins can be _inherited_ (passed on from your parents), e.g. cystic fibrosis.

Have a pop at this small quiz:

1) How many bases code for one amino acid?
2) What do mutagens do?

Genetic Engineering

Genetic Engineering is the Manipulation of Genes

1) _Genetic engineering_ is basically just _manipulating_ genes, e.g. altering DNA by _adding_ or _removing_ whole genes or parts of genes.
2) _Organisms_ that have had their _DNA altered_ are called _genetically engineered organisms_. Genetically engineered organisms can also be called _genetically modified organisms_ (GMOs) or _transformed organisms_.
3) Genetically engineered organisms can be _microorganisms_ (e.g. bacteria), _plants_ (e.g. rice) or _animals_ (e.g. sheep).

Genetic Engineering can be Very Useful

Genetic engineering is used to take _useful genes_ from one organism and add them into another. Useful genes are genes that code for _useful proteins_, or genes that code for proteins that produce _useful characteristics_. For example:

1) Genes that code for _hormones_, _enzymes_ and _antibiotics_ have been transferred into microorganisms, which then produce large quantities of these useful substances. E.g. genetically modified (GM) bacteria are used to produce _human insulin_ for people with _diabetes_.
2) Genes that improve _disease resistance_ and _drought resistance_ have been added to cereal plants.
3) _Sheep_ have been genetically engineered to produce useful substances in their milk. E.g. _human alpha-1-antitrypsin_ (used to treat the lung disease _emphysema_) is produced this way.

Some People are Concerned about Genetic Engineering

Not everyone's happy about genetic engineering or GMOs:
1) Some people don't think it's right or natural to manipulate an organism's genes.
2) Other people think GMOs like GM crops might not be safe to eat. However, there's currently no scientific evidence to suggest GM crops are unsafe to eat.
3) Others are worried that genes from GMOs could 'escape' into non-GMOs, causing problems. E.g. a herbicide resistance gene from a GM plant could escape into a weed, producing a weed that's resistant to herbicides.

See if you can answer these questions:
1) What is genetic engineering?
2) What is a genetically modified or transformed organism?
3) Give one reason why some people are concerned about genetic engineering.

Answers
1) Manipulation of genes.
2) An organism that has had its DNA altered.
3) Some people think it's not right or natural to manipulate an organism's genes / some people think GMOs like GM crops might not be safe to eat / some people are worried that genes from GMOs could 'escape' into non-GMOs, causing problems.

Genetic Engineering Techniques

First the Useful Gene is Cut Out Using Enzymes

1) Bacteria have enzymes called _restriction endonucleases_ that can _cut DNA_. Restriction endonuclease enzymes are often called _restriction enzymes_.
2) Restriction enzymes will _only cut_ DNA molecules at a _specific site_ — a specific _sequence of bases_ in the DNA, e.g. GAATTC.
3) _Different_ restriction enzymes cut DNA at _different_ sites, e.g. one might cut at GAATTC and another might cut at AAGCTT.
4) The enzymes _only cut_ at specific sequences because the _shape_ of the DNA strand with that sequence fits into their _active site_.
5) Purified restriction enzymes are used in genetic engineering to _cut out useful genes_ by cutting either side of them. For example, they can be used to cut out the gene for _insulin_ from a human DNA molecule:

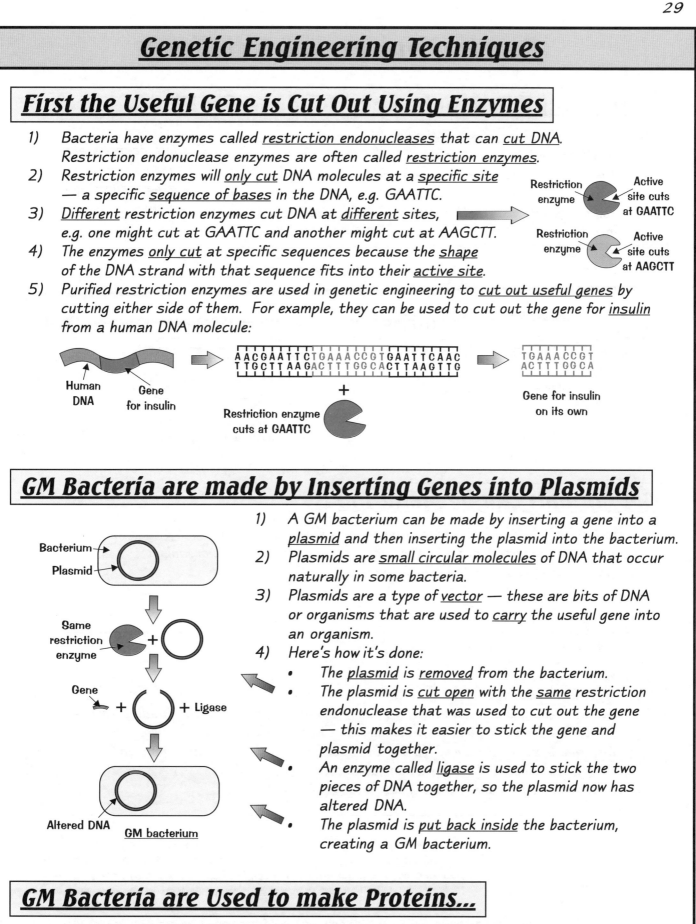

GM Bacteria are made by Inserting Genes into Plasmids

1) A GM bacterium can be made by inserting a gene into a _plasmid_ and then inserting the plasmid into the bacterium.
2) Plasmids are _small circular molecules_ of DNA that occur naturally in some bacteria.
3) Plasmids are a type of _vector_ — these are bits of DNA or organisms that are used to _carry_ the useful gene into an organism.
4) Here's how it's done:
   - The _plasmid_ is _removed_ from the bacterium.
   - The plasmid is _cut open_ with the _same_ restriction endonuclease that was used to cut out the gene — this makes it easier to stick the gene and plasmid together.
   - An enzyme called _ligase_ is used to stick the two pieces of DNA together, so the plasmid now has altered DNA.
   - The plasmid is _put back inside_ the bacterium, creating a GM bacterium.

GM Bacteria are Used to make Proteins...

1) GM bacteria are often created to make useful _proteins_ — e.g. GM bacteria that have altered DNA containing the gene that codes for _human insulin_.
2) The GM bacteria are grown in large containers so that they _divide_ and produce lots of the useful protein, using the inserted gene.
3) The protein can then be _purified_ and _used_.

Genetic Engineering Techniques

...But They can Also be Used to make GM Plants

1) If you want to produce a GM <u>plant</u>, you need to use a GM bacterium to create it.
2) The GM bacterium with the useful gene <u>infects</u> a plant cell in tissue culture.
3) The bacterium inserts the gene (e.g. for drought resistance) into the cell, so that the <u>plant cell is now genetically modified too</u>.
4) The cell is used to make an <u>entire organism</u>, which has the useful gene in every cell.

> GM bacteria are used as vectors to genetically engineer plants.

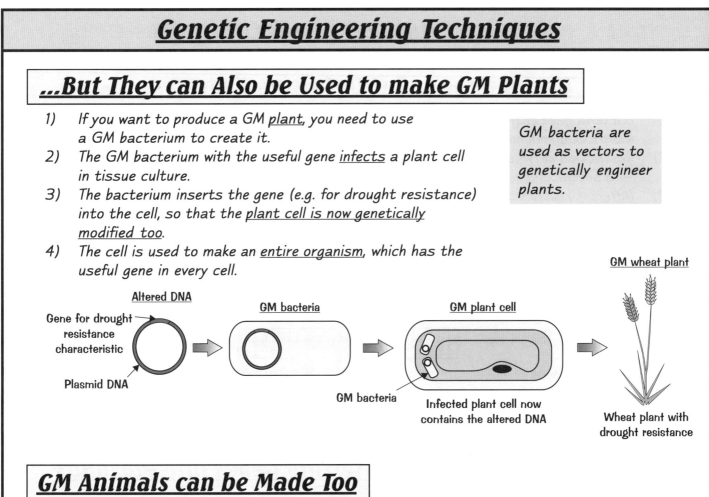

Altered DNA

Gene for drought resistance characteristic

Plasmid DNA

GM bacteria

GM plant cell

GM bacteria

Infected plant cell now contains the altered DNA

GM wheat plant

Wheat plant with drought resistance

GM Animals can be Made Too

To produce a GM <u>animal</u>, the gene of interest is <u>injected</u> into a <u>fertilised egg</u>. The egg is then inserted into a <u>mother</u> where it grows into a whole organism that will contain a copy of the gene in <u>every cell</u>.

See if you can answer these questions:

1) What is a restriction enzyme?
2) What is a vector?
3) Describe the steps involved in genetically engineering bacteria to include a new gene.
4) Bacteria have been genetically engineered to contain the human insulin gene. Describe what happens next to the GM bacteria in order to produce human insulin protein.
5) Briefly state how GM bacteria can be used to make a GM plant.
6) Describe how to make a GM animal.

Answers

1) An enzyme, found in bacteria, that cuts DNA.
2) Bits of DNA or organisms that are used to carry useful genes into an organism.
3) A plasmid is removed from the bacterium. The plasmid is cut open with the same restriction enzyme that was used to cut out the gene. Ligase is used to stick the two pieces of DNA together. The plasmid is put back inside the bacterium, creating a GM bacterium.
4) The GM bacteria are grown in large containers so that they divide and produce lots of human insulin. The human insulin is then purified for use.
5) The GM bacterium is used to infect a plant cell in tissue culture. The cell is used to make a new plant that contains the useful gene in every cell.
6) The gene of interest is injected into a fertilised egg. The egg is then inserted into a mother where it grows into a whole organism that has a copy of the gene in every cell.

Gel Electrophoresis and Genetic Fingerprinting

Gel Electrophoresis Separates Pieces of DNA

Sometimes a _mixture_ containing lots of _different sized_ pieces of DNA will need _separating_, e.g. you've _cut up_ a large piece of DNA using _restriction enzymes_ and you need to separate out the piece that _contains the useful gene_ you're after. _Gel electrophoresis_ (pronounced: elec-tro-for-e-sis) is a technique that separates pieces of DNA according to their _size_:

1) First a _gel_ is made — a _slab_ of a clear jelly that has _holes_ at one end.

2) The DNA is _mixed_ with a _fluorescent marker_ that _binds_ to the pieces of DNA, so they can be _seen under a UV light_. The DNA mixture is then _added_ to the holes in the gel.

3) A _charge_ is applied to the gel, so _one end is positive_ and _one end is negative_. DNA is _negatively charged_, which means it will move into the gel and _towards_ the _positive end_.

4) _Smaller pieces_ of DNA _move more quickly_ through the gel than larger pieces. So smaller pieces _move further_ through the gel.

5) The gel is left for a while and is then placed under a _UV light_ so the DNA can be seen — _smaller pieces_ of DNA will have moved the _furthest_ and so will be nearest the _bottom_ (positive end) of the gel. _Larger_ pieces of DNA will have moved the _least_ and so will be nearest the _top_ (negative end) of the gel.

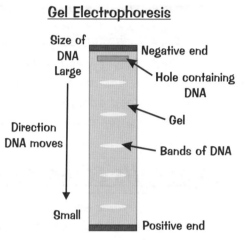

Gel Electrophoresis

DNA _size_ is measured in _bases_, e.g. ATTGCGG = _7 bases_ and 1000 bases = 1 _kilobase_ (often shortened to _1 kb_).

Everybody has Slightly Different DNA

All organisms of the _same species_ have _slightly different DNA sequences_ to each other, so everybody has _slightly different DNA_. If you _chopped up_ two different individuals' DNA and separated the pieces using gel electrophoresis, each gel would have a slightly different _pattern_ of DNA pieces because the DNA of the two individuals is slightly different. This is called _genetic fingerprinting_ (or _DNA fingerprinting_) — the pattern on the gel is the fingerprint. It can be used to _compare DNA samples_ for various reasons:

Genetic fingerprints show differences in DNA sequences found between genes, not differences in genes.

1) In _forensic science_ — e.g. to see if a DNA sample from a _crime scene_ matches that from a _suspect_. If it matches, it _links_ the suspect to the crime scene.

2) To determine _relationships_ — e.g. to see if two people are _related_. The _more similar_ the two fingerprints, the _more closely related_ the two people are.

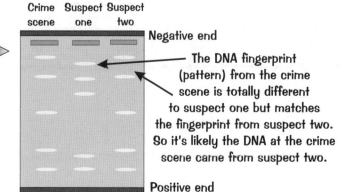

The DNA fingerprint (pattern) from the crime scene is totally different to suspect one but matches the fingerprint from suspect two. So it's likely the DNA at the crime scene came from suspect two.

Stem Cells

Stem cells Can Become Any Type of Body Cell

1) Most of the cells in your body are <u>specialised</u> to carry out a particular <u>job</u> — e.g. red blood cells are specialised to <u>carry oxygen</u>. They have lots of <u>haemoglobin</u> (the protein that carries oxygen) and no nucleus so there's more room for haemoglobin.

2) <u>Stem cells</u> are <u>unspecialised cells</u> that can divide and then <u>differentiate</u> (specialise) into <u>any type of cell</u>.

3) During the <u>very early stages</u> of development, when an <u>embryo</u> is only 4-8 cells big, the cells are <u>all stem cells</u> (called <u>embryonic stem cells</u>). The cells then start to <u>divide and differentiate</u> into all the different types of cell found in the body.

4) All adults still have <u>some</u> stem cells in their body, but they <u>aren't</u> as <u>flexible</u> — they can <u>only</u> differentiate into a <u>limited range of cell types</u> (i.e. not all types). E.g. <u>bone marrow</u> in adults has stem cells that divide and differentiate into cells of the <u>blood</u> and <u>immune system</u> (including red blood cells), but <u>can't</u>, for example, specialise into nerve cells.

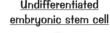
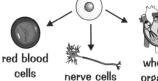

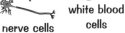

Undifferentiated embryonic stem cell

red blood cells / nerve cells / whole organs

Undifferentiated adult stem cell (e.g. in bone marrow)

red blood cells / nerve cells / white blood cells

Stem cells Could be Really Useful in Medicine

Because embryonic stem cells can differentiate into any type of cell, it's thought they could be used to <u>grow cells</u>, <u>tissues</u> or even <u>whole organs</u> to <u>replace</u> those that are <u>damaged or diseased</u>. E.g. to replace <u>nerve cells</u> in people who have spinal injuries or <u>heart tissue</u> for people who have had heart attacks. But some people are <u>against</u> embryonic stem cell research as it <u>can involve</u> the <u>destruction</u> of an <u>embryo</u>. Adult stem cells <u>aren't as flexible</u> as embryonic stem cells — but scientists are working on ways to make these cells grow into any cell type too.

Plant Stem Cells can be Used to Make Clones

1) Plants have stem cells too, e.g. at the tips of their <u>stems and roots</u>.
2) <u>All</u> plant stem cells can develop into <u>any plant cell type</u> (like embryonic stem cells).
3) This means plant stem cells can be used to grow new plant <u>cells</u>, <u>tissue</u> or even a <u>whole new plant</u> if they're given the <u>right conditions</u> (e.g. the right growth <u>hormones</u>).
4) Using a few plant stem cells to grow an entire new plant is called <u>tissue culture</u>.
5) The new plant produced is a <u>clone</u> of the original <u>parent</u> as it's a <u>genetically identical copy</u> of the parent (every cell has <u>identical DNA</u> to the original parent).

Some new processes and words to learn. Can you remember them?

1) In gel electrophoresis, what is the DNA mixed with to make it visible under UV light?
2) Why does DNA move towards the positively charged end of a gel?
3) What is a stem cell?
4) What is a clone?

Answers
1) A fluorescent marker.
2) Because it's negatively charged.
3) An unspecialised cell that can differentiate into any cell type.
4) A genetically identical copy, e.g. of a plant.

Reliability and Validity

Evidence is Reliable If It Can be Repeated

Scientific evidence needs to be reliable (or reproducible). If it isn't, then it doesn't really help you. When you're doing an investigation, you need to repeat your experiment several times to <u>make sure</u> your results are reliable — you should get round about the same answer each time.

<u>RELIABLE</u> means the results can be consistently reproduced in independent experiments.

> *Example*
>
> In the 1990s, some scientists claimed there was a link between the hepatitis B vaccine and multiple sclerosis. It was big news — some countries, e.g. France, withdrew the vaccine. But other scientists just couldn't get the same results — they weren't reliable. Since then other scientists have shown that there's no link between the hepatitis B vaccine and multiple sclerosis.

Evidence Also Needs to be Valid and Representative

Collecting reliable data is important, but if the data doesn't answer your original question, it won't be any use. You need to think about <u>what</u> data to collect to make sure your results will be valid.

<u>VALID</u> means that the data is reliable <u>AND</u> answers the original question.

It's also important that you base your data on a big enough sample. The danger with a small sample is that your data might only be true for that sample — you won't be able to extend your results to other situations because they aren't <u>representative</u> of the whole population.

Controlling All the Variables is Really Hard

The difficulty with a lot of scientific investigations is that it's very hard to control all the variables that might (just might) be having an effect.

> *Example*
>
> Studies have shown a correlation between the variables "increase in average temperature" and "reduction in the number of bees". But this doesn't prove that increasing temperature is causing a reduction in the number of bees — other explanations are possible.
> For example, there may be a new disease that's killing the bees, or the number of flowers may be decreasing because of increasing pollution, so the bees have less to feed on.

In the lab it's different — scientists can control the variables so that the only one that changes is the one they're investigating — all the others are kept constant. In experiments like this, you can say that one variable <u>causes</u> the other one to change because you have made sure that nothing else could be causing the change.

You Don't Need to Lie to Make Things Biased

When you write up your results, it's important to give a <u>balanced</u> view of the data so that the reader can make up their own mind about it. People who want to make a point can sometimes present data in a <u>biased</u> way to suit their own purposes — e.g. by only using the bits of data that support their argument, or by phrasing things in a leading way.

Graphs and Relationships

Repeating an Experiment Lets You Find a Mean Result

If you repeat an experiment, your results will usually be slightly different each time you do it.
You can use the _mean_ (or average) of the measurements to represent all the values.
The more times you _repeat_ the experiment the more _reliable_ the average will be.
To find the mean:

ADD TOGETHER all the data values then _DIVIDE_ by the total number of values in the sample.

Graphs Are Used to Show Relationships

Once you've collected all your data and worked out the mean results, you need to _analyse_ it to find any relationships between the variables. The easiest way to do this is to draw a graph, then describe what you see.

Example

Sharon did an experiment to see how the rate of photosynthesis changed depending on the temperature. She measured the rate of photosynthesis at 9 different temperatures. Sharon has drawn a graph to see if the two variables are related.
She has included a line of best fit, which shows the correlation between rate of photosynthesis and temperature.

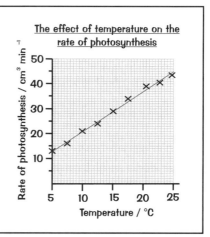

The effect of temperature on the rate of photosynthesis

Drawing Graphs is Easy — When You Know How

Graphs are really useful for showing whether variables are related, so make sure you know how to draw them.

1) Get your _axes_ the right way round — the thing you change (the independent variable) goes on the x-axis. The thing you measure (the dependent variable) goes on the y-axis.

2) Think about the _scale_ to use on each axis. You should make the most of the space you have by spreading the points out so that you can see what's going on.

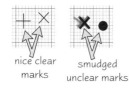

nice clear marks   smudged unclear marks

3) _Plot_ the data points — use a sharp pencil and make a neat little cross.

4) Give your graph a _title_ so it's clear what it's about.

5) Draw a _line of best fit_ through your data. Try to draw the line through or as near to as many points as possible, ignoring anomalous results. Don't just connect up your data points — the line of best fit is meant to show the general trend in the data points, not their exact locations.

Correlation and Cause

Lines of Best Fit Are Used to Show Trends...

The line of best fit on Sharon's graph shows that as the temperature is _increased_, the rate of photosynthesis also _increases_. This is called a _positive correlation_. The data points are all quite close to the line of best fit, so you can say the correlation is _strong_. If they were more spread out, the correlation would be _weak_.

 Variables can also be _negatively correlated_ — this means one variable _increases_ as the other one _decreases_. Look at the way the line of best fit _slopes_ to work out what sort of correlation your graph shows.

Sometimes the graph won't show any clear trend and you won't be able to draw a line of best fit. In this case, you say there's _no correlation_ between the variables.

...and Estimate Values Between Data Points

When you do an experiment it's impossible to measure every data point. Instead, you can use the line of best fit to _estimate_ values _in between_ the data points that you actually measured — this is called _interpolation_. Or, you can use it to estimate values _outside_ the range you measured — this is _extrapolation_. The method is the same for both — you draw a line from one axis to the line of best fit, then turn and go straight to the other axis and read off the value you end up at.

The estimates you get from _interpolation_ are usually fairly _trustworthy_ — if you've measured a series of points that show a clear trend, it's unlikely that anything weird will happen between them. _Extrapolation_ can be a bit _dodgy_ because it assumes your trend will continue in the same way. Take Sharon's graph — extrapolation predicts that a temperature around 30 °C would produce a rate of photosynthesis of about 50 cm^3 min^{-1}. It might, but then again it might not — you can't rely on the result.

Correlation Doesn't Always Mean Cause

Be careful what you _conclude_ from an experiment — just because two variables are correlated, it doesn't necessarily mean that one _causes_ the other.

In lab-based experiments like Sharon's, you can say that the independent variable causes the dependent variable to change — the increase in temperature _causes_ an increase in the rate of photosynthesis. You can say this because everything else has _stayed the same_ — nothing else could be causing the change.

Outside a lab, it can be much harder:

> Example
>
> Polly measured the amount of rain and the abundance of plants in different meadows, to see whether the two are related. Her results show a positive correlation between the variables — where the amount of rain is highest, the abundance of plants is also highest.

From Polly's results, you can't say that a lot of rain causes more plants to grow. Neither can you say that more plants cause more rain. It could be either way round... or one change might not cause the other at all — you just can't tell.

Index